CUTHB THE CROC

144

BY SALLY LUNT

ILLUSTRATED BY ALEX CRUMP

First published in Great Britain in 2020

ISBN 978-1-8380274-0-7

Printed and bound by Quorum Print Services, Cheltenham, GL51 8PL

CUTHBERT THE CROC
MATHEMATICAL ADVENTURES BOOK 1

CONTENTS

Goes on
and on!

Cuthbert the Croc loved numbers. One morning, he woke up feeling very excited. He was going to the Number Convention. The convention started at 9 o'clock and Cuthbert was planning to walk to it. He started to get dressed and began counting.

"One and two and three and four,
I love numbers, let's count some more...
five and six and seven and eight.
Is that the time, I might be late!"

Cuthbert had always dreamt of finding the end of the number line. He counted all the time. So far, no matter how high he had counted, he had never found the biggest number. He was certain, however, that it must be just around the corner. He was hoping the convention would help him.

"Even though I count all day long,
I never finish my numbers' song.
Perhaps today I'll meet a friend,
who can help me reach the end!"

He had got so carried away, that he hadn't noticed the time. He rushed downstairs for his breakfast.

When it was time to go, his mother said:

"Now you must be on your way.
I hope you have a lovely day.
Here's your phone, your lunch and a snack.
Put them safely in your pack."

As he kissed her goodbye, she told him the route to take.

The route went through
the jungle, over a watering
hole and down some rapids.
Cuthbert waved goodbye and
started counting again. He
remembered her words as he
went.

"Twenty-one, twenty-two, twenty-three."
Into the jungle, past the tallest tree.

Page 2+1=3

"Thirty-four, thirty-five, thirty-six."
Through the long grass, avoiding the tics!

"Forty-seven, forty-eight, forty-nine."
Splash through the pool, the water's divine.
"Fifty, fifty-one and fifty-two."
Don't play with the troll, whatever you do.

"Sixty-three, sixty-four, sixty-five."
Swim down the rapids and you'll arrive.

Cuthbert carried on counting as he swam down the rapids.

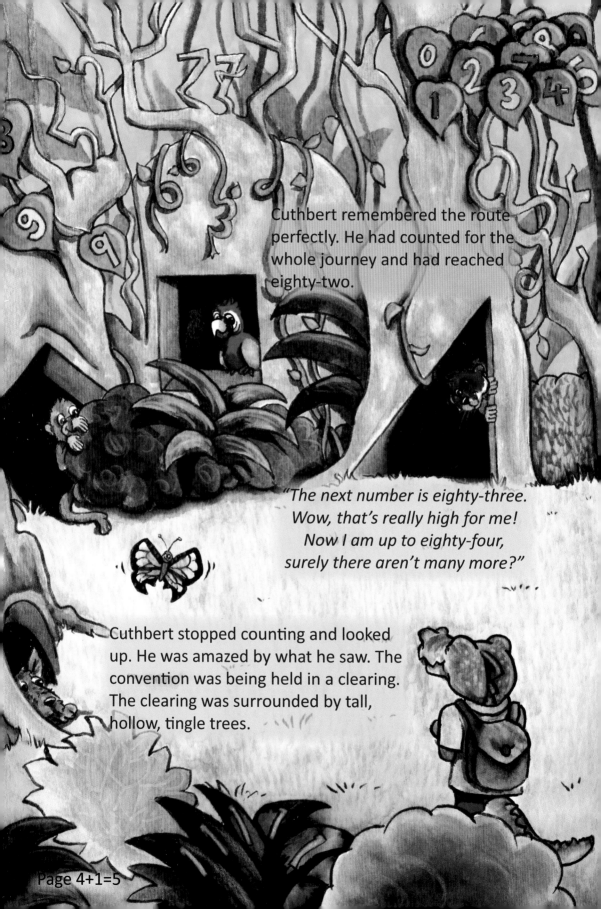

Cuthbert remembered the route perfectly. He had counted for the whole journey and had reached eighty-two.

"The next number is eighty-three.
Wow, that's really high for me!
Now I am up to eighty-four,
surely there aren't many more?"

Cuthbert stopped counting and looked up. He was amazed by what he saw. The convention was being held in a clearing. The clearing was surrounded by tall, hollow, tingle trees.

At the entrance to the clearing was the biggest tree. Inside its hollow sat a tall stoat. He was wearing a pink waistcoat with numbers all over it. When it was Cuthbert's turn to show his ticket, the stoat said:

"Hello and welcome. My name is Sid.
This clearing's named after the great Euclid,
a mathematician who loved geometry.
A magical spot; I'm sure you'll agree.
The tingle trees are home to each talk.
Please use this tablet and the app called chalk."

Cuthbert was also given a name badge. He attached it securely. Then he made his way inside. As he walked, he started counting again. He got so caught up with it that he wasn't watching where he was going. He was brought back with a bump as he crashed into Maureen the Mouse. He said:

> *"I'm very sorry, are you ok?*
> *I hope I haven't spoilt your day.*
> *I'm focused on counting all the time,*
> *to fulfil a special dream of mine!"*

Maureen looked thoughtfully at Cuthbert. She introduced herself and told him that she was not hurt. Maureen was the Head of the Number Agency. This meant she knew a lot about numbers. She looked at his name badge and asked about his special dream. He answered:

"The biggest number is my quest
and even though I try my best,
I find myself a little stuck:
meeting you is a stroke of luck."

Maureen was about to answer Cuthbert but before she could, he said:

"You see, everything was going fine
but then I got to ninety-nine.
I cannot picture what might be next
and I'm feeling very vexed.
Is this the end of the number line?
Have I fulfilled that dream of mine?"

Maureen gave a little smile, shook her head and said:

"Sorry no, and I have to say,
that you can't, there is no way.
If you count 'till eternity,
at the end, you'll still not be.
On and on indefinitely,
numbers grow and grow you see."

Cuthbert listened to Maureen very carefully. He was puzzled by the word indefinitely and said:

"What's the meaning of that word?
It isn't one I've ever heard."

Maureen explained that indefinitely means the numbers go on forever and ever. She told him that a bigger number can always be found by adding one more.

"Whatever number you have in mind,
add one on and you will find,
a bigger number does exist:
I promise, it's an endless list."

Cuthbert considered this for a moment and then shook his head and said:

"Maureen, I think you must be wrong
and I will finish my numbers' song.
I am certain that it will all be fine
when I know what's after ninety-nine."

Maureen smiled and explained that one hundred came after ninty-nine. She told Cuthbert that she had found it by adding one to ninety-nine.

Cuthbert thought for a moment and then said:

"I've got it, one hundred and ninety-nine.
At last, I've reached the end of the line."

Maureen was impressed with Cuthbert's thinking and said:

"Two hundred is next and it's bigger still.
My approach has worked and always will!
Just add one on in order to get,
a number that is bigger yet."

Cuthbert looked panicked for a moment. Then he thought carefully and said:

"What about nine-hundred and ninety-nine?
Surely that is the end of the line!"

Maureen was impressed again but she shook her head and said:

"Cuthbert, your thought is mighty fine,
but one thousand is next in line.
Quick on its heels is one thousand and one,
the numbers really do run and run.
After that, it's one thousand and two,
You've spotted the pattern, haven't you?"

Cuthbert thought carefully and then said:

"Got it, one thousand, nine hundred and ninety-nine.
There's no way you'll beat that number of mine!"

However, Maureen said:

"I'm afraid I can, just as before,
two thousand is made, by adding one more."

Cuthbert and Maureen continued like this for quite some time. Every time Cuthbert thought of a new number, he was sure he had reached the end of the number line. But Maureen was always able to come up with a bigger number by adding one more. Cuthbert realised that Maureen was right. Numbers really do go on indefinitely.

> *"Whatever number that I choose,*
> *I'll never win, but always lose.*
> *You'll add one more and, magically,*
> *a bigger number there will be."*

Cuthbert sat down on the jungle floor looking very sad indeed. Then he began to cry. His dream of reaching the end of the number line had been dashed.

"Oh no, what will I do now" he wailed
"I'm sad to see that I have failed.
I lived to find the biggest number,
and dreamt about it in my slumber."

Page 18+1=19

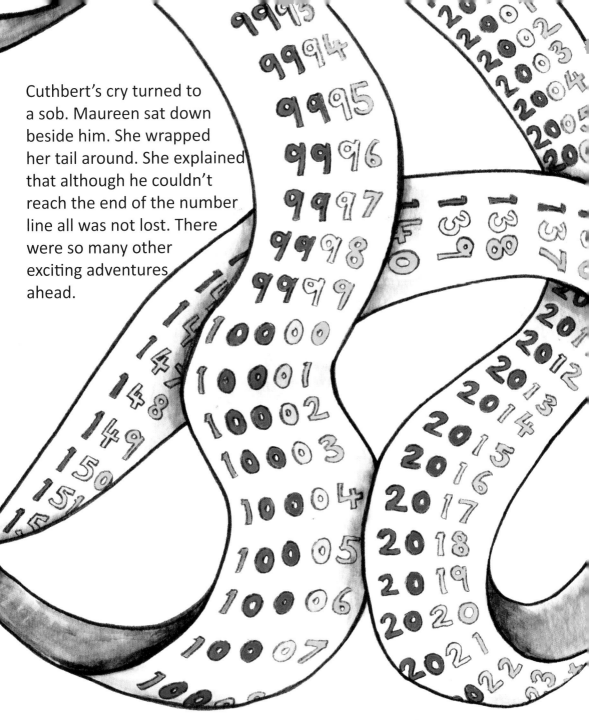

Cuthbert's cry turned to a sob. Maureen sat down beside him. She wrapped her tail around. She explained that although he couldn't reach the end of the number line all was not lost. There were so many other exciting adventures ahead.

"Cuthbert, I know that it looks bad
but there is no need to be sad.
The never-ending number line
really is a favourite of mine.
Numbers are special in many ways;
you'll still have plenty to fill your days."

Maureen handed Cuthbert a handkerchief. Cuthbert wiped his eyes and blew his nose. Then he looked up at Maureen with a hopeful smile and said:

"One door has closed but now I see
many more open to me.
I'm excited by what you say,
will you help me find my way?"

Maureen beamed at Cuthbert. She had always loved numbers too. She was excited to have found someone else who wanted to learn about them. She hoped that Cuthbert would come to the Summer Fête in a few weeks' time.

"Yes of course, I'll help you;
I would be delighted to.
Now, have you learnt to count in twos?
I find primes can ease the blues.
Addition is also really great
and would be handy at the fête."

Cuthbert grinned from ear to ear. He loved numbers even more now.

"Thank you, Maureen, that is good to hear.
What a relief, I'll no longer fear.
I like the sound of addition best,
how thrilling to have another quest."

Maureen was delighted. She invited Cuthbert to listen to her talk. She was going to explain how the Egyptians had used numbers to build the Pyramids. Cuthbert skipped along as Maureen led the way.

Your turn...

Cuthbert has come up with these numbers. Can you find the number that is worth one more than each of these?

75
133
572
1027
4891
39
69
99
299
499
799
2999
3999
5999
9999

Start at the beginning of the list again. This time can you find the number that is worth two more than each of these?

Cuthbert has come up with these other numbers. Can you find the number that is worth one less than each of these?

8

15

47

51

72

84

101

112

350

500

992

2991

2990

4001

8540

Start at the beginning of the list again. This time can you find the number that is worth two less than each of these?

Parents

Begin

Help your child to answer the questions on the previous pages.

Embed

Help your child to become familiar with numbers by

- looking at what number comes next. For example, what comes after 99, 199, 999, 9999...? Get them used to working with numbers as digits and as words.
- asking your child what is the biggest number in the hundreds, thousands, ...?
- getting your child to come up with their own questions.
- playing "The Biggest Number" Game: ask your child if they think they can come up with a bigger number than you. Then ask if they would like to go first or second. They might initially say they want to go first but will soon realise it is to their advantage to go second.

Extend

Help your child further by

- looking at finding numbers that are worth 3 more or 3 less, then 4 more or 4 less and so on.
- looking at the continuum of numbers from 1 to 2. This is quite advanced because you will need to introduce decimals. The continuum between 1 to 2 is infinite.

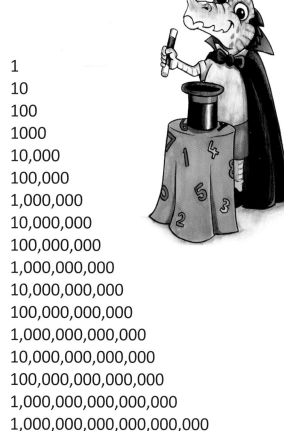

1	One
10	Ten
100	One hundred
1000	One Thousand
10,000	Ten Thousand
100,000	One Hundred Thousand
1,000,000	One Million
10,000,000	Ten Million
100,000,000	One Hundred Million
1,000,000,000	One Billion
10,000,000,000	Ten Billion
100,000,000,000	One Hundred Billion
1,000,000,000,000	One Trillion
10,000,000,000,000	10 Trillion
100,000,000,000,000	100 Trillion
1,000,000,000,000,000	1 Quadrillion
1,000,000,000,000,000,000	1 Quintillion
1,000,000,000,000,000,000,000	1 Sextillion
1,000,000,000,000,000,000,000,000	1 Septillion

What's the next number in this sequence? Investigate. You could also investigate where the names for these numbers come from.

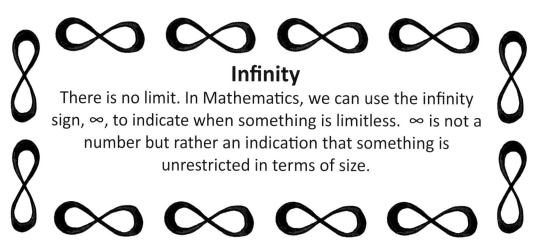

Infinity

There is no limit. In Mathematics, we can use the infinity sign, ∞, to indicate when something is limitless. ∞ is not a number but rather an indication that something is unrestricted in terms of size.

Why not visit Cuthbert at
WWW.CUTHBERTTHECROC.CO.UK
to learn even more about numbers and practise some sums...

CUTHBERT THE CROC

SWITCHES THINGS AROUND

Cuthbert the Croc was eating his breakfast. He was feeling very excited. Today, he was helping at the Number Agency Summer Fête. Cuthbert was running the toy stall with his friend Betty the Badger. They would have to add up the cost of the toys that customers wanted to buy. It was a big responsibility. Cuthbert was especially excited to practise his addition. He and Betty had been learning to add up at school with Mrs Bha and loved it. Cuthbert kissed his mother goodbye and skipped off to the fête singing as he went.

"I'm so excited, I cannot wait
to be with Betty at the fête.
I'm going to have such a ball
practising addition on the toy stall.
Adding up the numbers will be fun;
then I'll look around when my work is done."

The fête was being held in the Euclidean clearing, deep in the jungle. Cuthbert knew the way and decided to practise his addition on his journey. First, he had to pass the tallest tree.

"I know the route, it's easy for me,
so I'll focus on adding everything I see.
Oh look, two robins and a lark up high,
I think they're playing tag in the sky.
That's two add one, which makes three.
I'm right on track; there's the tallest tree."

Cuthbert walked on some more and came to the long grass. He peered in and saw some commotion.

"Three little mice playing with a rat,
perhaps they can shelter under my hat.
After a rest, the game begins once more.
Three add one, well that makes four."

Cuthbert already knew that numbers go on indefinitely. He understood that the next number is always made by adding one more on.

After the long grass was the pool. Cuthbert was nervous about the troll who lived there but he liked paddling in the water.

*"I'll jump straight in and splash around
and see what creatures can be found.
Four white swans and two coot chicks.
Four add two, I know is six."*

Mrs Bha had explained how to add on two. Cuthbert knew adding two to a number was the same as adding one and then another one.

Finally, Cuthbert was at the rapids where he met a family of turtles and a bull frog going to the fête.

At the end of the rapids, they would see the first tingle tree and the clearing.

"At last down the rapids, we must go.
The Euclidean clearing is just below.
Six happy turtles and a bull frog too.
Six add one is easy to do."

"That's seven altogether but don't forget me.
Eight of us are swimming to the tingle tree."

Cuthbert saw the clearing as he came down the rapids. It was a beautiful open space. Around the outside were lots of hollow trees. Inside the hollow of each tree was a stall. Cuthbert found the tree containing the toy stall. Cuthbert saw Betty looking for the stall. He waved and called to her. As she arrived, he said:

"I hope all of our customers will buy
two toys at once so we can try
to practise our newly learned addition:
what a super mathematical mission."

It was still a few minutes until the fête started.
Cuthbert and Betty had a little time to play.
Betty pretended to be a customer buying toys.

"Ok" said Betty "let's have a practice go;
I'll pick this toy soldier and the blue yo-yo.
You add up the prices and then let me know
how much in total it is that I owe."

Cuthbert looked at the price of each item and said:

"Ok Betty, well let me see,
seven add one, that's easy for me.
The total amount to pay is eight;
oh look Betty, they're opening the gate."

As the gate opened, lots of animals rushed in. Cuthbert had his first customer a few minutes later. It was one of the turtles from the rapids. Cuthbert said:

"Hello Sir, are you ready to pay?
I'm Cuthbert and I'm helping out today.
I see your items cost five and one,
that's six to pay – phew, my first sale's done!"

Just as Cuthbert finished, Betty began serving her first customer. She said:

"Hello I'm Betty, can I help you?
The truck is six and the book is two,
which makes a total of eight to pay;
thank you Sir and enjoy your day."

After a quick sip of water, Cuthbert had a new customer. It was Sid the Stoat. Sid was wearing his bright pink waistcoat with numbers all over it. Cuthbert said:

"Good morning, I hope you are enjoying the fête,
these toys you've chosen are really great.
It's two for the duck and the car is eight;
I will add them up, please could you wait?"

Cuthbert started to add two and eight. After a few moments, he began to huff and puff. Then he started to go red in the face. He mumbled:

"Oh dear me, I'm in a dreadful state.
I start at two and try to add on eight.
But I get all muddled in my head,
it's so much harder than Mrs Bha said."

Betty saw that Cuthbert was struggling. She asked if she could help. Cuthbert was grateful and told her the sum.

"The answer to two add eight is what we need.
Hmm, it is a very tricky sum indeed.
At this rate, it'll take me all day;
if only we knew of a faster way."

Betty began to count but it wasn't long before she began to panic too.

"Oh no, I'm sorry but I've lost count;
I feel the pressure beginning to mount.
Cuthbert, what are we going to do?
We need some help, who can we turn to?"

Just then Maureen the Mouse arrived. Maureen was the Head of the Number Agency. She had encouraged Cuthbert to help at the fête. She saw that Cuthbert and Betty looked worried. She decided to see if she could help.

"Hello you two, how are you getting on?
Why are your faces so very, very long?"

Cuthbert and Betty were in a panic. They both tried to explain their problem to Maureen but they were in too much of a state. Maureen said:

"When faced with a problem, as a rule,
I try to keep both calm and cool.
Breathing deeply or counting to ten
or going for a walk helps me then
to think more clearly so I can find
a neat solution and peace of mind."

Cuthbert counted to ten and Betty took some deep breaths. Straight away they felt calmer and were able to explain their problem to Maureen. After they finished Maureen said:

> *"When you are adding two and eight,*
> *there's no need to get in a state.*
> *By switching the two numbers round*
> *an easier sum will be found!"*

Cuthbert and Betty beamed with relief. They knew that they would now be able to serve Sid. Together they said:

> "Maureen, thank you for saving us,
> now we can serve Sid without a fuss.
> Two add eight equals eight add two,
> Look, we both know what to do.
> Sid, it's a total of ten to pay,
> Thanks for waiting for us today."

Cuthbert wondered if they could use this approach all the time. He asked Maureen:

"Does this method work every time?
What about the sum of three add nine?
Is it the same as nine add three?
Is twelve the answer? Can it be?"

Maureen smiled and said:

*"Gosh Cuthbert you are very bright,
you got that sum completely right.
You can always switch the numbers round,
mathematically, this trick is sound."*

Maureen left and Cuthbert started serving another customer.

"These items are favourites of mine.
Now let me see, that's two add nine.
That is a very difficult sum,
oh dear, oh dear, what can be done?"

Cuthbert was starting to panic. Then he remembered what Maureen had said. He counted to ten and then said:

"It's all ok, I know what to do.
I'll switch them round to nine add two.
Summing them is easy peasy,
and now I don't feel at all queasy!"

Cuthbert and Betty had time at the end of the fête to look around. Cuthbert found some gifts that he wanted to buy for his mother. The stall holder was Sid the Stoat whom he had served earlier.

*"Oh these colourful seashells are ornate;
a gift for my mother from the fête.
The pink costs two and the white costs seven,
another sum - I'm in number heaven!
Two add seven is no match for me
I'll switch them round and now can see
that seven add two makes nine to pay;
I've really had a brilliant day."*

Cuthbert paid Sid and said goodbye to Betty and Maureen. Then he raced off home singing as he went:

"Switching numbers has been ace,
but now it's time for me to race.
My brother's home having tea
with our friends from Italy.
If I'm quick, we just might fit
in a game of 'Double It'."

Your turn...

Betty also went shopping at the end of the fête. She bought a milkshake that cost £2 and a puzzle that cost £5. This is how could we write this sum using a mathematical sentence:

£2+£5=£7

Or just using numbers:

2+5=7

Remember if the sum seems difficult, you can try to switch it around to find the answer:

£5+£2=£7 or 5+2=7

Can you help Cuthbert & Betty with these sums? Try to give your answers as mathematical sentences.

1. The car is £3 and the book is £7. What is the total?
2. The cherry is 5p and the orange is 8p. What is the total?
3. The gloves cost £2 and the hat cost £9. What is the total?
4. The duck is £2 and the doll is £5. How much do they owe?
5. The soldier is £4 and the science lab is £8. How much do they owe?

Sid wants to buy 3 toys. A car which costs £4, a boat that costs £6 and a doll that costs £7. Can you work out how much he owes?
Can you write this using a mathematical sentence?

Parents

Begin

Help your child to answer the questions on the previous page and to write a mathematical sentence to describe each situation. Then encourage them to make up their own examples.

Embed

Help your child to become confident with addition by

- making up more examples like those on the previous page.
- making up harder examples by introducing numbers such as 10, 20, 30 or even 13, 14, 15. Add a number 1-9 to 10, 20, 30 in the first instance. Once your child is confident with this you could move on to the teens.
- asking your child to make up their own more complicated examples. Get them to write them out in words first and then as a mathematical sentence.

Extend

Help your child further by

- playing card games. They are an excellent way of introducing addition. Start with Golf – a fun game with strategy that will help your child to understand chance. It also provides an opportunity for them to practise their addition by working out everyone's scores. They won't even realise that they are practising because it is such fun!
- looking at number sentences where one of the numbers is missing, e.g. 6+   =14.
- starting to look at subtraction as the reverse of addition. For example, if 6+4=10 then we can say that...10-4=6 and 10-6=4.

CUTHBERT THE CROC

SEES DOUBLE
SEES DOUBLE

Cuthbert the Croc was walking home feeling very happy. He had spent the day helping on the toy stall at the Number Agency's Summer Fête. He had been adding up prices of toys for customers all day long. He was now a bit of an expert when it came to addition! He was looking forward to getting home for some tea. He was also hoping to play 'Double It' with his big brother Claude and their Italian friends. Cuthbert did not know how to play 'Double It'. It involved numbers and looked like a lot of fun. When he got home, Cuthbert saw they had started to play and said:

"Excuse me Claude, would it be ok,
for me to join; I'd love to play?
I promise that I will be really good,
playing by the rules, as all crocs should."

Claude and their friends were a few years older than Cuthbert. They had played 'Double It' a lot. They were worried that Cuthbert might not be able to keep up. Claude said:

"I'm not sure that it's a good idea,
we are used to playing here.
This means the game is very fast
and you may end up coming last."

Cuthbert was desperate to play. He begged Claude to let him. In the end, Claude agreed and explained the rules.

"You turn over the card for us all to see.
Focus on the number, that is the key.
The aim of the game is to double the number,
yet there's no time for you to slumber.
The first to get it wins the card:
it sounds easy, but it's hard."

Cuthbert wasn't put off by what Claude said. He had had such success with his addition at the fête that he was confident he would be able to understand. He thought to himself:

"Numbers are such a passion of mine,
I'm sure this game is going to be fine.
I'll watch the first round and see how to play,
then nothing will be able to stand in my way."

When everybody was ready, they began to play.

"Ok" said Claude "it is time to start,
turn the top card, can you please Mart?
It is an eight and it needs doubling,
a tricky start – oh this is troubling."

Everyone was thinking about the answer. They were all desperately trying to get there first. After only a couple of seconds, Mart said:

"Sixteen, yes; I got it first!
I'm so excited that I might burst.
I can't wait 'till we turn the next one,
this game is always brilliant fun."

Cuthbert was confused. He couldn't quite see what was happening. How did double eight become sixteen? He decided to see what happened in the next round. He was sure that he would be able to understand. It was Bella's go to turn over the top card this time. She said:

"Ok, next round, is everyone ready?
I feel nervous and my hand's unsteady.
Right, here we go and it's a three,
I know it's six – that's a win for me!"

Cuthbert was shocked at how quickly Bella had got the answer. He just couldn't understand how to double. He watched a couple more rounds, but he couldn't spot the pattern. He was starting to feel a bit sad. He was finding the game very difficult. He was coming last, exactly as Claude had said. Very quietly, so no one would hear, Cuthbert said:

"Oh dear me, I should be glad
but I am feeling very sad.
I just don't know what to do
and feel like crying; boo-hoo-hoo."

Cuthbert decided that it would be best to go for a walk. He hoped that by clearing his head, it would help him to figure out how to double. He didn't want to spoil the game. He told Claude that he fancied a walk because it was such a lovely day. As he walked, he said to himself:

"Three doubled is six, how does that work?
I can't see a pattern – where does it lurk?
Help, someone help me, what must I do?
If only I could double, I'd stop feeling blue!"

Just then Cuthbert saw Maureen the Mouse. Maureen was the Head of the Number Agency. She was making her way home from the fête. Maureen had helped Cuthbert with his addition at the fête. She was very impressed with how well he had done. She was delighted to see him again and said:

"Are you still on cloud nine?
Your addition was divine.
Oh dear me, you look so sad.
What has happened that is bad?"

Cuthbert explained to Maureen that he had been playing 'Double It'. He told Maureen that he hadn't been able to join in because he didn't know how to double a number.

"Playing a game, I got into trouble.
The problem is, I cannot double.
It's a shame, it should've been fun
but I felt sad and had to run.
The walk has helped to clear my mind
but a pattern I still cannot find."

Maureen and Cuthbert sat down on a bench by a plum tree.

Maureen was impressed that Cuthbert had tried to help himself and explained that doubling a number is the same as adding the number to itself.

"Cuthbert, don't worry, this is easy to fix.
Imagine that you want to double six.
Add six to six and the answer will be,
crystal clear for you to see."

Cuthbert thought for a moment and said:

"Is the answer twelve? If that's true,
then I do see what I have to do.
Now suppose I want to double four,
I would start at four and add four more.
Four add four, I know makes eight,
and if that's right, I'll feel just great."

Maureen was pleased. She knew that Cuthbert had understood. She said:

"Well done Cuthbert, you're quite right.
Gosh you are extremely bright.
And now I think that you are fit,
for another game of 'Double It'!
Before you go, I must say
one more thing, it'll make your day!"

Maureen went on to explain that doubling is the same as multiplying by two.

"If you want to multiply by two,
Choose a number, any number will do!
Let us suppose that, just as before,
You have chosen the number four.
We both need four plums, here's my pile.
Pop yours here too, upon the sundial.
That's two piles of four, now add the lot
and four times two is what you've got."

Cuthbert beamed. He knew that he was ready.
He thanked Maureen for all her help.

"Oh Maureen, you are wonderful and kind,
but excuse me please as I'm off to find
if they are still playing 'Double It'
now I'm not afraid – not a bit.
Double five is ten, double one is two,
yes I am ready, many thanks to you."

When he got back home, there wasn't anybody around. Cuthbert's hopes of a game were dashed. Then he heard some footsteps coming up the garden path. He opened the front door and saw Claude and their Italian friends. They were worried about Cuthbert and had been out looking for him.

"We are sorry that you were sad,
we were feeling pretty bad.
So we came to find you and say,
let's play something else today."

Cuthbert was delighted that they were back and said:

"Thank you, that's kind indeed
but there really is no need.
I can double numbers now,
Maureen the Mouse taught me how!
I would love to play one more round.
What do you think? How does that sound?"

Everybody was delighted. They sat down for another game of 'Double It'. This time, Cuthbert went first.

"I've got a nine and I know what to do.
I will double it or times it by two.
Nine add nine is what I need,
it's eighteen - and I'm in the lead."

Everyone clapped and cheered. Cuthbert had understood. They continued the game until all the cards had gone. Cuthbert managed to double every number that came up. Quite often, he got to the right answer before the others. Claude told everyone to count their cards to see who had won. Once everybody had counted, Claude said:

"I've got eight but it's not enough to win,
compared to Claire's pile, mine is thin."
"Well I've got fourteen cards" said Claire
"But I spy even more over there.
Cuthbert, how many cards have you got?
It looks like you have got a lot!"

Cuthbert grinned sheepishly.

"I've got sixteen and I think I've won.
Thanks for the game, it's been such fun."

It was now quite late. As a special treat, they were all sleeping under the stars together. They ate their supper and picked up their sleeping bags.

Then they headed out into the jungle. They would be sleeping at the Archimedes' sky lodge. It was only a short walk to the sky lodge. The moon shone brightly to light their way. As they walked, Cuthbert practised doubling.

$$7+7$$
$$=$$
$$7×2$$

"What a magical evening: it is a full moon.
We'll be at sky lodge really quite soon.
It's named after a mathematician who loved the sky.
Looking up at its beauty, I understand why.
There, it's the Plough: seven stars shining bright.
Double seven is fourteen, I know that I'm right."

They reached the sky lodge and found their pod. They got inside and settled in their sleeping bags. The stars and moon were shining brightly above them.

They looked for different constellations. Thinking about how Archimedes had done the same thing many years ago, Claude said:

"I spy with my little eye,
a constellation nearby.
It forms the letter W,
can you all find it too?"

Cuthbert loved the stars. He knew which
constellation Claude meant and said:

"Made from five stars, it's Cassiopeia;
she was a queen; can you all see her?
It's just to our left – above that forked tree,
I can move to one side to help you see.
Five stars doubled is as easy to do
as five add five or five times two.
They are all the same, they all make ten;
I hope we'll come back here again."

Cuthbert was starting to feel sleepy. He had enjoyed the day very much. He was particularly delighted that he knew how to play 'Double It'. He was keen to teach Betty the Badger, his friend from school. He was seeing her next weekend at the Number Quiz. Just as he was drifting off to sleep, he thought about all the fun they would have.

*"There will be lots of excitement next weekend
at the number quiz, where I'll see my friend.
I think I'll teach her how to play;
it's bound to be a brilliant day.
I hope we'll double at the quiz,
given that I am such a whizz.
But now it's late, and the stars will keep
us safe and sound, whilst we sleep."*

Your turn...

Can you Double these numbers?
4
7
10
12
15
17
21

We can write doubling as a mathematical sentence:
$$7+7=14$$

Can you write a mathematical sentence for doubling each of the numbers above?

Now multiply each of the numbers below by two:

3

5

7

8

14

17

We can write 7 multiplied by two as a mathematical sentence:

$$7×2=14$$

Do you see that double seven equals fourteen and that seven times two equals fourteen?

Can you write mathematical sentences for the other numbers above?

Parents

Begin

Help your child to answer these questions and to write a mathematical sentence to describe each situation. Then encourage them to make up their own examples.

Embed

Help your child to understand doubling by

- playing 'Double It'. Use a standard pack of cards. Each number card takes its value and you could let the Jack=11, Queen=12 and King= 13. You might want to limit the number of cards you use initially and build up to using the bigger numbers.
- asking your child to make up their own more complicated examples with higher teen numbers. Get them to write them out in words and then as a mathematical sentence.

Extend

Help your child to go beyond doubling by

- playing "Triple It" or "Ten times" or "Five times". The same as 'Double It' but you multiply the number by 3, 10 and 5 respectively.
- looking at number sentences where one of the numbers is missing, e.g.   ×2=10. Fill in the missing number.